Gold Stars

Wipe-clean
Reading

PaRragon

Bath · New York · Cologne · Melbourne · Delhi
Hong Kong · Shenzhen · Singapore

Helping your child

- Remember that the activities in this book should be enjoyed by your child. Try to find a quiet place to work.

- Your child does not need to complete each page in one go. Always stop before your child grows tired, and come back to the same page another time.

- It is important to work through the pages in the right order because the activities get progressively more difficult.

- Your child will begin by recognizing pictures and move on to recognizing words. Help your child to read the words and recognize the rhymes as you work through the book.

- The answers to the activities are on the inside of the back cover.

- Always give your child lots of encouragement and praise.

This edition published by Parragon Books Ltd in 2017

Parragon Books Ltd
Chartist House
15–17 Trim Street
Bath BA1 1HA, UK
www.parragon.com

Written by Frances Mackay
Illustrated by Simon Abbott
Educational consultant: Janet Rose

ISBN 978-1-4748-7785-5

Printed in China

Contents

Find it

Look at the picture.
Tick each thing as you find it in the picture.

boat ☐   seahorse ☐   anchor ☐

diver ☐   jellyfish ☐   fish ☐

Note for parent: This activity gives your child practice in identifying shapes and objects, which helps prepare for reading. Make up a story about the picture.

Draw a ring around the picture that is different in each line.

  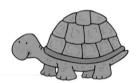

Note for parent: Recognizing shapes and objects that are the same helps with pre-reading skills.

5

Match the shapes that are the same.
One has been done for you.

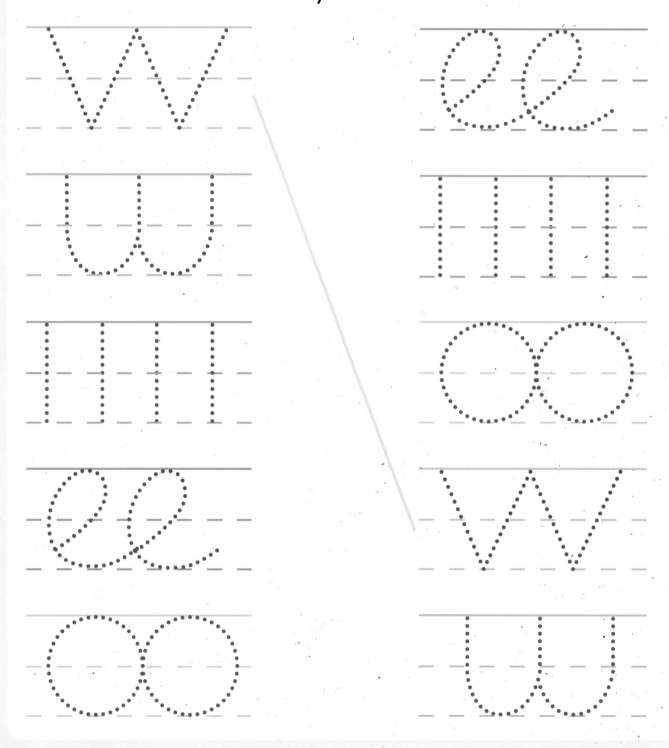

Begins with s

Look at the pictures. Say what they are.
Match the pictures that begin with the sound **s**
to the letter **s**.
One has been done for you.

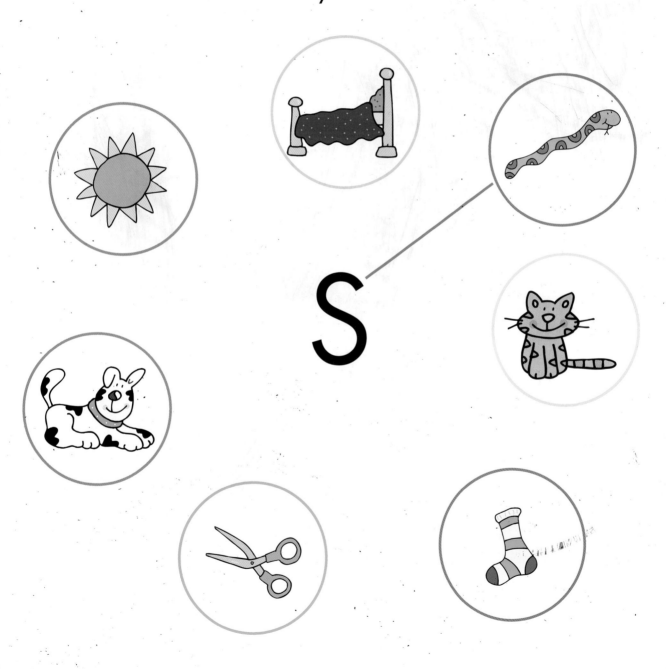

Note for parent: This activity helps your child to hear the difference between beginning sounds, and to identify sounds that are the same.

7

Words that rhyme

Look at the pictures. Say what they are.
Draw lines to match up the words that rhyme.

clock

bee

pen

hat

snail

hen

whale

cat

sock

key

Note for parent: This activity helps your child recognize word endings that sound the same (rhyme), even though they may be spelled differently.

Odd one out

Look at the pictures. Say what they are.
Draw a ring around the picture that does not
rhyme in each row.

cat

hat

snake

boat

house

mouse

frog

log

cake

carrot

bat

parrot

bear

chair

fish

Match the beginning sounds

Say the name of each picture.
Draw a line to match the beginning sound to the correct letter.

m
d
g
o
c
e
r
b

Note for parent: This activity gives your child practice in identifying beginning sounds and their corresponding letters.
Say each letter sound (not the letter name) as you point to each letter,

Write it

Say the name of each picture.
Write the beginning letter sound for each one.
Choose from the letters in the box.

k u f h l w z j

Note for parent: This activity gives your child further practice in identifying beginning sounds and their corresponding letters. Say each letter sound (not the letter name) as you point to each letter.

11

Draw a line to match the words to the pictures.

sun

bed

dog

pen

tap

rat

mop

Note for parent: Look at the pictures first. Say what they are. Ask your child to find the word with the correct beginning sound and then sound out the rest of the letters.

Which word?

Which word?
Draw a ring around the correct word to match each picture.

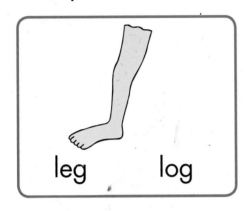

leg   log

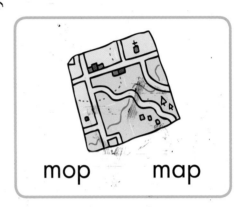

mop   map

fin   fan

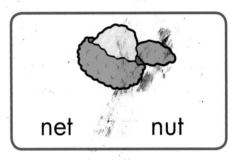

net   nut

cat   cot

bag   bug

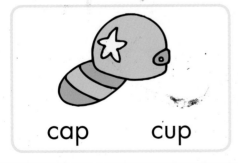

cap   cup

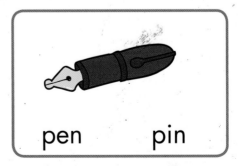

pen   pin

Finish the words

These pairs of words rhyme.
Choose a letter to complete each word.
Say the rhymes.

b c e g h k m n p r s t

_ing   _ing   _at   _at

_oat   _oat   _ose   _ose

_ate   _ight   _ie   _ie

Match the words

Draw a ring around the word that is the same as the first in each row.

| big | bike | big | dog | dig |

| book | took | book | king | bell |

| boy | boy | toy | bed | bee |

| house | mouse | house | hat | man |

| dad | did | mum | dog | mad |

| clock | sun | sock | rock | clock |

| play | door | day | plug | play |

Note for parent: This activity gives your child practice in identifying words that are the same. Can your child find words that rhyme in each row?

Party time

Draw a line to match the labels to things in
the picture.
Make up a story about what is happening in
the picture.

table   cake   balloon   parcel

jelly   melon   milk   hat   girl

Note for parent: This activity gives your child practice in reading a picture story. If necessary read the words to your child, then ask your child to find the objects in the picture.

Look at the pictures. Circle the correct answers.

big   small

Circle the big animal.

happy   sad

Circle the sad face.

short   tall

Circle the tall clown.

shut   open

Circle the open door.

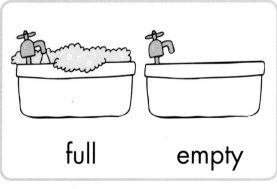

full   empty

Circle the full bath.

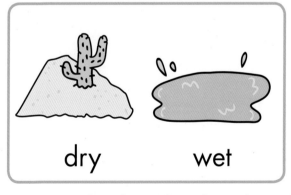

dry   wet

Circle the dry land.

Draw a picture to tell a story in each row.

Draw what they are looking at.

Draw what the diver sees in the water.

Draw something you would eat at a picnic.

Note for parent: This activity gives your child practice in inventing simple stories. Talk about what could happen in each one.

What is happening?

Look at the picture.
Answer the questions.

Draw a ring around the correct answer.

Is the cat asleep?	yes	no
What is the girl doing?	singing	playing drums
Is it a sunny day?	yes	no
Where is the teddy?	on the mat	in the box

Tricky words

Some words are tricky to read!
Read the tricky words and match them to a word that rhymes.

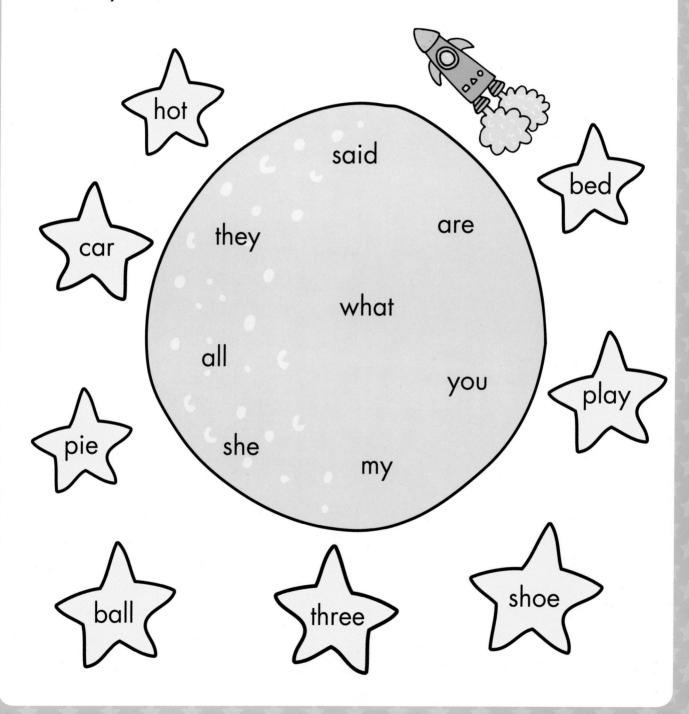

hot

said

bed

car

they

are

what

all

you

play

pie

she

my

ball

three

shoe

Note for parent: This activity helps your child recognize some tricky, high-frequency words. Read each tricky word to your child and ask them to find the word that rhymes. Explain that they do not always end in the same letters.

More tricky words

Draw lines to match the words that are the same.

the

the

some

of

from

this

this

some

me

from

of

one

one

do

have

do

have

me

Make a story

Look at the three pictures to see what is happening. Write the numbers 1 to 3 in the boxes to show their correct order.

Draw or write what you think they found.

Note for parent: This activity gives practice in sequencing a story. Talk about what is happening in each picture and what might happen in the end.

Finish the poem

Choose words from the box to complete the poem.
Make sure the poem rhymes.

today	floor	most	bed
bee	best	now	mat

A is for apple that grows on my tree

B is for banana, butterfly and _____

C is for cuddle that I give to my cat

D is for dog who sleeps on the _____

E is for eggs that I eat on toast

F is for football, the sport I love _____

Note for parent: This activity gives further practice in identifying words that rhyme. Read the poem to your child then ask them to choose words that rhyme to complete the lines.

23

Find these words in the puzzle.
Draw a ring around each one you find.
Look across and down.

boy

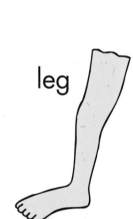

pie

c	b	o	y	m	o
a	e	n	k	u	v
t	d	e	h	d	b
w	r	p	i	e	z
d	r	a	t	n	o
l	e	g	m	d	o

leg

hit

rat

mud

Note for parent: This activity gives your child a fun way to look at three-letter words.